## Walkthrough

This is another Josie story – can you remember any others?

Let's read the title: 'Josie Goes On Holiday'.

What sort of holiday are they going on? (*camping*)

Has anybody here been on a camping holiday?

## Walkthrough

Let's read the blurb together.

What sort of things might they get up to on a camping holiday?

G000019511

## Walkthrough

Read the title.

This is a picture of a map.

Let's have a look at it – what sorts of activities might Josie and Ravi do which are on the map?

**Walkthrough**

Where are they?

What are they doing here?

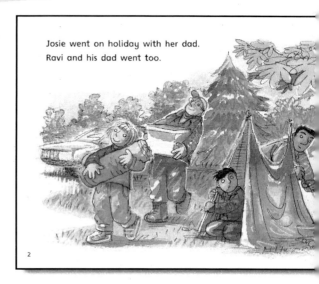

Josie went on holiday with her dad.
Ravi and his dad went too.

2

👁 **Observe and Prompt**

### Word Recognition

- Check the children are using their decoding skills to tackle more difficult words, such as 'Josie' and 'first'.

- Prompt the children to break the word 'holiday' down into three syllables, before blending the whole word together.

- Check the children can read 'walk'. Model the reading of this word if necessary.

2

## Walkthrough

Where do you think Josie's dad is going to take them?

Why are they looking at the map?

On the first day, Josie's dad took Josie and Ravi on a long walk.

3

 **Observe and Prompt**

### Language Comprehension

- Ask the children what the characters did on the first day of their holiday.
- Ask the children why the characters might need a map.
- Have any of the children in the class been camping?

## Walkthrough

Is Dad enjoying the walk?

How can you tell?

How do Josie and Ravi feel? Why?

Josie's dad walked very fast.
"This is fun!" he said.

## 👁 Observe and Prompt

### Word Recognition

- Help the children with the 'ed' suffix at the end of 'walked' and 'tired' if they have difficulty with these words.

- If the children have difficulty reading 'couldn't', model the blending of this word for them.

- Help the children with the 'ai' sound in 'wait' if they struggle.

## Walkthrough

What is the problem with Josie and Ravi?

What do you think they are saying to Josie's dad?

Josie and Ravi couldn't walk so fast.
"I'm tired!" said Josie.
"Wait for us!" said Ravi.

5

 **Observe and Prompt**

### Language Comprehension

- Check the children are reading the dialogue with expression, taking note of punctuation.
- Ask the children who is walking the fastest.
- Ask the children if Josie and Ravi can keep up with Dad.
- Ask the children what Ravi shouts to Josie's dad.

## Walkthrough

Where are they now?

Do you think they had a good time?

How do they feel?

What do you think they might do next?

They got back to the tents.
"Did you have a good time?" asked Ravi's dad.

6

## Observe and Prompt

### Word Recognition

- Check the children are using their decoding skills to tackle the more difficult words on these pages, such as 'time' and 'very'.

## Walkthrough

What did Josie and Ravi do? Why?

"We did, but we're very tired,"
said Josie and Ravi.
Then they fell asleep.

7

 **Observe and Prompt**

### Language Comprehension

- Check the children are reading with appropriate expression.
- Ask the children why they think Josie and Ravi fell asleep.
- Do the children think Josie and Ravi are enjoying the holiday?

## Walkthrough

The next day Ravi's dad takes them somewhere.

What are they going to do?

The next day, Ravi's dad took Josie and Ravi canoeing. "This is fun!" said Ravi's dad.

8

 **Observe and Prompt**

### Word Recognition

- If the children have difficulty with the words 'canoeing' and 'canoe', model the blending of these words for them. Explain that 'oe' makes an 'oo' sound here.

- Prompt the children to break the word 'getting' down into two syllables, before blending the whole word together.

- Check the children can read the sight words 'is', 'said', 'we', 'to', 'go' and 'so' with confidence.

## Walkthrough

Do you think Ravi's dad is having fun?

What is happening to Josie and Ravi?

How do they feel?

The canoe went very fast.
"I'm getting wet!" said Josie.
"Do we have to go so fast?" asked Ravi.

9

## 👁 Observe and Prompt

### Language Comprehension

- Check that the children have established the pattern of the text.
- Ask the children what the characters are doing now.
- Have any of the children in the class been in a canoe?

## Walkthrough

Do you think they had a good time?

How do they feel?

What happened when they got back to
their tent?

They got back to the tents.

"Did you have a good time?" asked Josie's dad.

"Yes, but we're very wet," said Josie and Ravi.

Then they fell asleep.

10

##  Observe and Prompt

### Word Recognition

- If the children have difficulty with the word 'horse-riding',
  encourage them to break the word down into its three
  parts before reading the whole word.

- Check the children can read the 'ed' suffix at the end
  of 'wanted'.

## Walkthrough

Which day of the holiday is this?

What did Josie and Ravi want to do?

How do you think the two dads feel?

The next day, Josie and Ravi wanted to go horse-riding.

11

 **Observe and Prompt**

### Language Comprehension

- Ask the children how they think Josie and Ravi felt after they went canoeing.

- Ask the children what Josie and Ravi wanted to do the next day.

- Have any of the children in the class ever been horse-riding?

**Walkthrough**

What are Ravi and Josie doing now?

How are Josie and Ravi feeling?

Josie and Ravi liked riding the horses.
"This is great fun!" said Josie.
"Come on!" said Ravi.

12

 **Observe and Prompt**

**Word Recognition**

- If the children have difficulty reading 'didn't' and 'couldn't', ask them to split the words up and read the first parts 'did' and 'could', then to look at the word endings.
- Check the children can read 'horses' and 'horse' using their decoding skills.

**Walkthrough**

How do you think the dads feel?

What is their problem?

What do you think they are saying to the children?

Josie's dad didn't like his horse.
He couldn't get it to go.
Ravi's dad didn't like his horse.
He couldn't get it to go.
'Wait for us!' they said.

13

 **Observe and Prompt**

**Language Comprehension**

● Observe the children reading with expression, taking note of exclamation marks.

● Ask the children if Josie's dad and Ravi's dad like horse-riding.

● Do the children think Josie and Ravi like horse-riding?

● Who do the children think is going fastest today?

13

## Walkthrough

How do you think the children feel?

How do their fathers feel?

What do you think Josie and Ravi want to do tomorrow?

When they got back to the tents,
Josie and Ravi weren't tired.
"I love horse-riding!" said Josie.
"So do I!" said Ravi.
"Can we do it again tomorrow?"

## 👁 Observe and Prompt

### Word Recognition

- Check the children can read the word 'weren't' using their decoding skills.
- Check the children can read the sight words on this page with confidence ('to', 'do', 'we').
- Prompt the children to break the word 'tomorrow' down into three syllables, before blending the whole word together.

### 👁 Observe and Prompt

**Language Comprehension**

- Ask the children who is tired today.
- Do the children think the dads want to go horse-riding again tomorrow?

**Walkthrough**

How do the two dads feel?

Do you think they will go horse-riding again?

Why not? (*The fathers are too tired.*)

Do you think this is a good ending?

"We're too tired!" said the two dads.

16

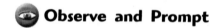

## Observe and Prompt

### Language Comprehension

- Check the children read with appropriate expression.
- Check the children appreciate the humour of this ending.